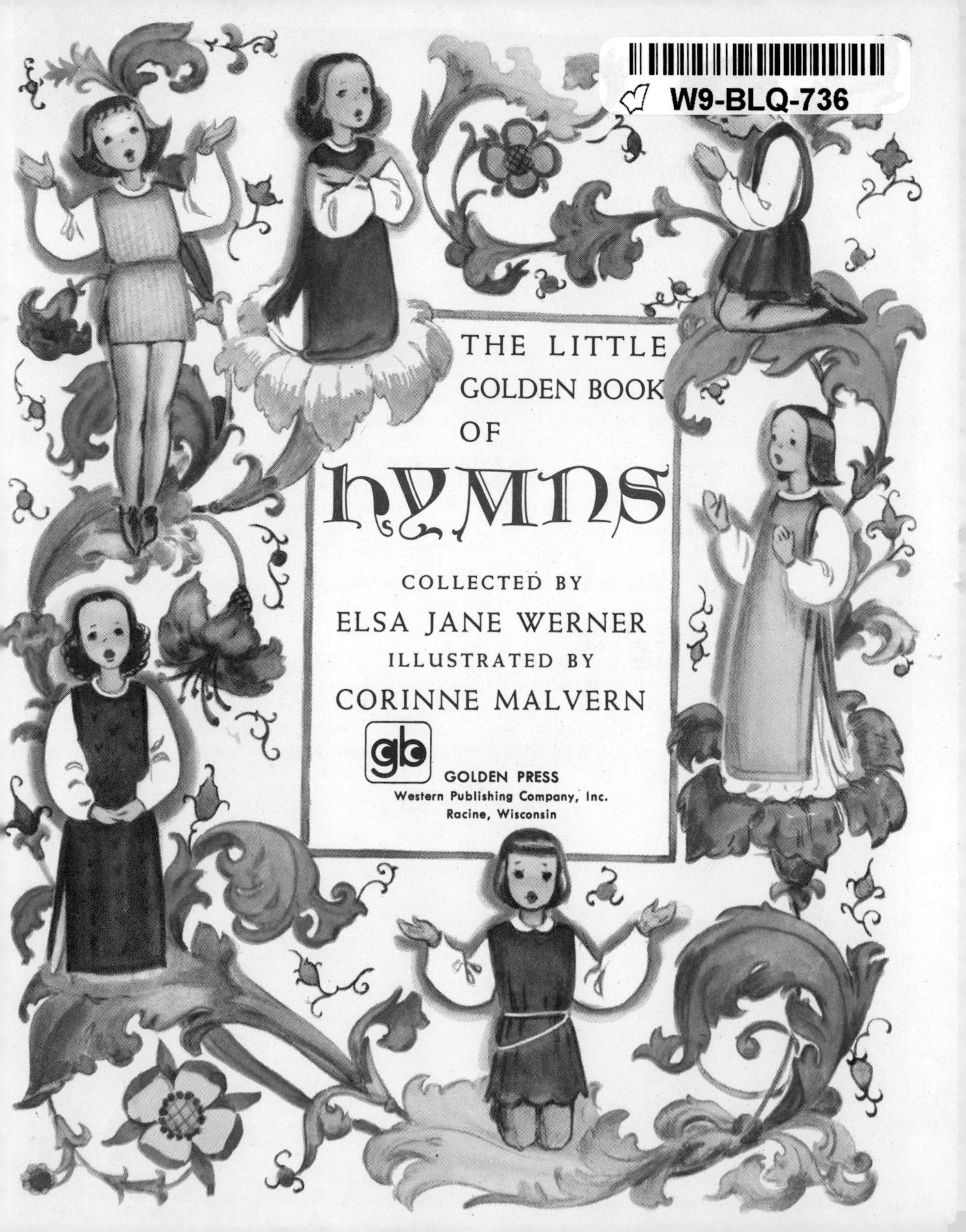
THE LITTLE
GOLDEN BOOK
OF
HYMNS
COLLECTED BY
ELSA JANE WERNER
ILLUSTRATED BY
CORINNE MALVERN
gb
GOLDEN PRESS
Western Publishing Company, Inc.
Racine, Wisconsin
W9-BLQ-736

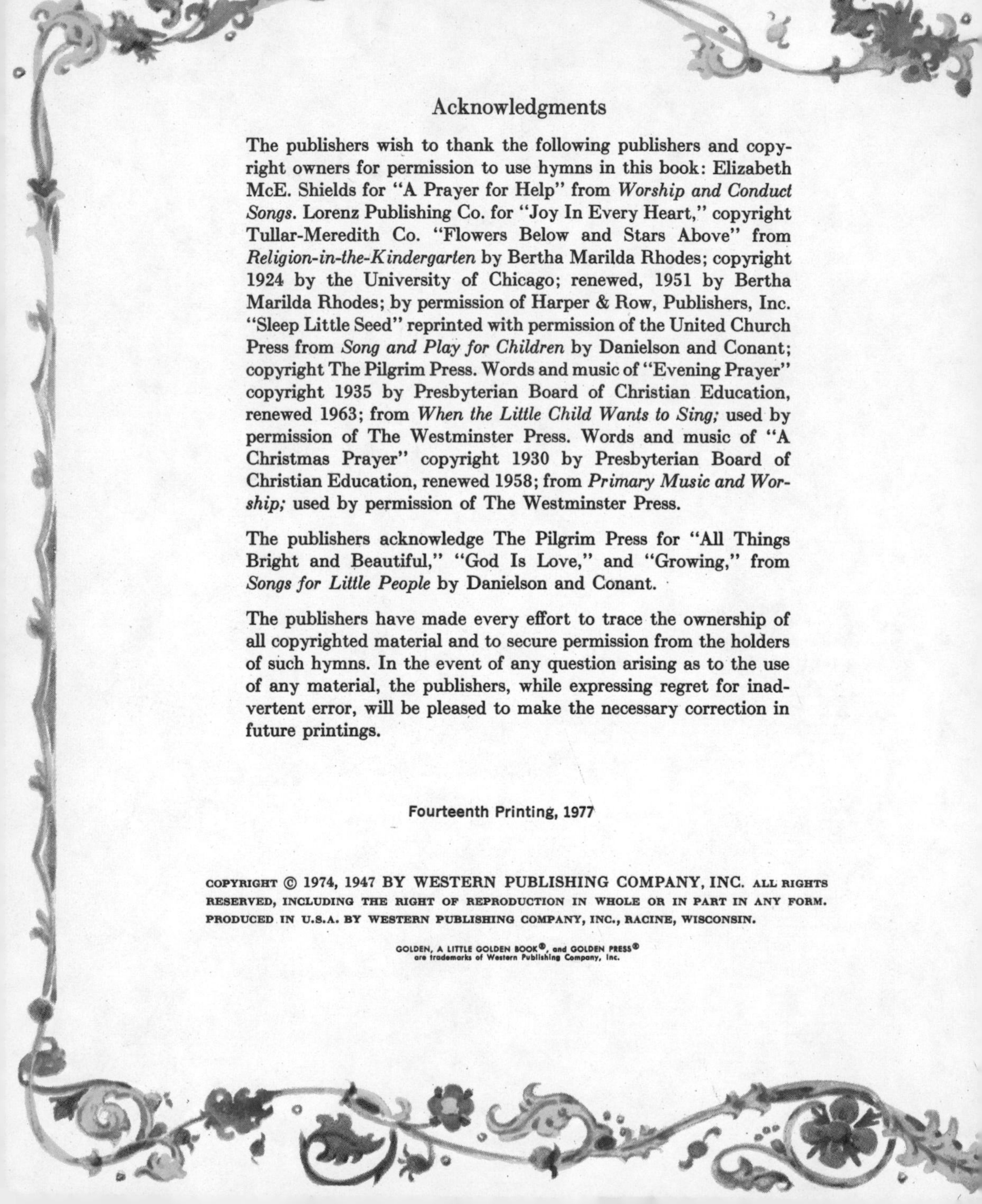


## Acknowledgments

The publishers wish to thank the following publishers and copyright owners for permission to use hymns in this book: Elizabeth McE. Shields for "A Prayer for Help" from *Worship and Conduct Songs*. Lorenz Publishing Co. for "Joy In Every Heart," copyright Tullar-Meredith Co. "Flowers Below and Stars Above" from *Religion-in-the-Kindergarten* by Bertha Marilda Rhodes; copyright 1924 by the University of Chicago; renewed, 1951 by Bertha Marilda Rhodes; by permission of Harper & Row, Publishers, Inc. "Sleep Little Seed" reprinted with permission of the United Church Press from *Song and Play for Children* by Danielson and Conant; copyright The Pilgrim Press. Words and music of "Evening Prayer" copyright 1935 by Presbyterian Board of Christian Education, renewed 1963; from *When the Little Child Wants to Sing;* used by permission of The Westminster Press. Words and music of "A Christmas Prayer" copyright 1930 by Presbyterian Board of Christian Education, renewed 1958; from *Primary Music and Worship;* used by permission of The Westminster Press.

The publishers acknowledge The Pilgrim Press for "All Things Bright and Beautiful," "God Is Love," and "Growing," from *Songs for Little People* by Danielson and Conant.

The publishers have made every effort to trace the ownership of all copyrighted material and to secure permission from the holders of such hymns. In the event of any question arising as to the use of any material, the publishers, while expressing regret for inadvertent error, will be pleased to make the necessary correction in future printings.

**Fourteenth Printing, 1977**

# A Prayer for Help

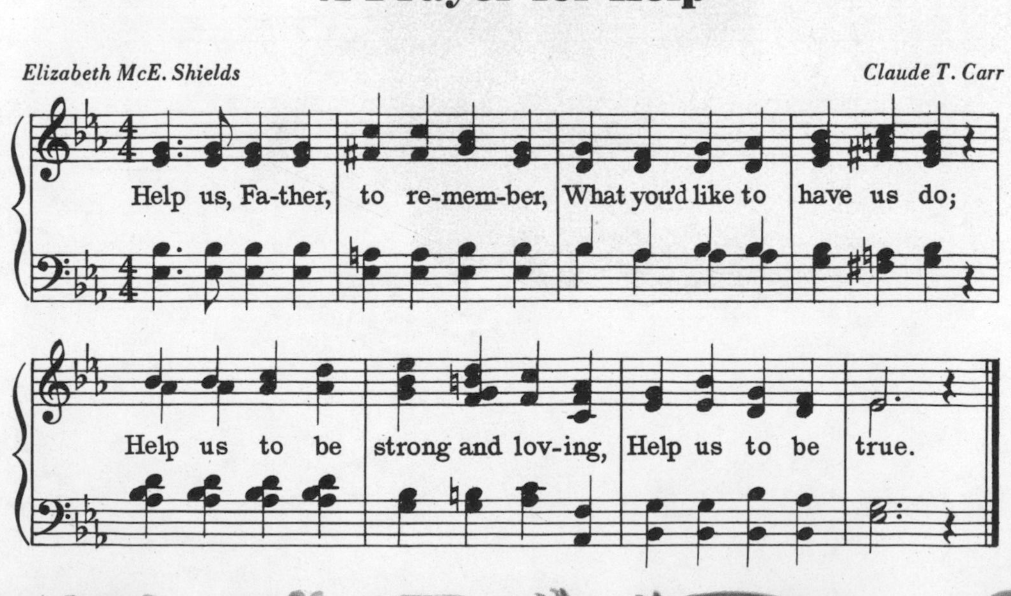

The Creation
J. B. W.
Words and Music by Johnie B. Wood
And God said the sun should shine, The rain should fall, the flow'rs should grow, And God said the birds should sing, And it was so, was so.
And God said the grass should grow, The trees bear fruit, the winds should blow, And God said the streams should flow, And it was so, was so.

Jesus Loves Me
Anna B. Warner
William B. Bradbury
Je - sus loves me! This I know, For the Bi - ble tells me so;
Lit - tle ones to Him be - long, They are weak, but He is strong.

CHORUS
Yes, Je - sus loves me, Yes, Je - sus loves me,
Yes, Je - sus loves me, The Bi - ble tells me so.

All Things Bright and Beautiful
Cecil Frances Alexander
Adapted from a Danish Folk Song
Each lit - tle flower that o - pens, Each lit - tle bird that
The pur- ple - head - ed moun - tain, The riv - er run-ning
The cold winds in the win - ter, The pleas - ant sum-mer
He gave us eyes to see them, And lips that we might
sings, God made their glow-ing col - ors, He made their ti - ny wings.
by, The sun- set and the morn-ing red, That bright-en up the sky.
sun, The ripe fruits in the gar - den, He made them ev - 'ry one.
tell The good-ness of the Fa - ther, Who do - eth all things well.

Refrain
Yes, all things bright and beau - ti - ful, All crea-tures great and
small, And all things wise and won-der-ful, The Lord God made them all.

God Is Love
Frances Weld Danielson
Grace Wilbur Conant
Lis-ten to our Eas-ter song, "God is love," "God is love,"
Now and all the win- ter long, "God is love."

Flow-ers wake that safe were hid-den, Birds come back as they are bid-den,
Chil-dren sing their Eas-ter song, "God is love."

# Joy in Every Heart

Praise, praise the Lord a-bove, For these gold-en days.
Praise the Lord, O come and praise the Lord, And tell His won-drous ways.

# Flowers Below and Stars Above

# Sleep, Little Seed

# Downy Little Snowflakes

# A Christmas Prayer

I'll Be a Sunbeam
Nellie Talbot
E. O. Excell
Je-sus wants me for a sun - beam, To shine for Him each day;
Je-sus wants me to be lov - ing, And kind to all I see;
In ev-'ry way try to please Him, At home, at school at play.
Show-ing how pleas-ant and hap - py His lit - tle one can be.
18

CHORUS
A sun-beam, a sun-beam, Je-sus wants me for a sun-beam; A
sun-beam, a sun-beam, I'll be a sun-beam for Him.

Growing

Grace Wilbur Conant
A lit - tle rain and a lit - tle sun, And a lit - tle pearl - y
A lit - tle work and a lit - tle play, And lots of qui - et
dew, And a push - ing up and a reach - ing out, Then
sleep; A___ cheer - ful heart and a sun - ny face, And
leaves and ten - drils all a - bout, And that's the way the
les - sons learned and things in place, Ah! that's the way the
flow - ers grow, Don't you know? Don't you know? And
chil - dren grow, Don't you know? Don't you know? Ah!
f>
mp

that's the way the flow-ers grow,
that's the way the chil-dren grow,
Don't you know?
Don't you know?

# Away in a Manger

*Words and Music by Martin Luther*

# Evening Prayer

# Contents